How to Be a scientist at home

How to

Be a scientist at home

John Tuey and David Wickers

STUDIO VISTA London

VNR **VAN NOSTRAND REINHOLD COMPANY** New York

Acknowledgments

Drawings and diagrams are by Sharon Finmark. The photograph of the compass on page 50 appears by permission of Henry Browne & Son Ltd. The authors would also like to express their thanks to Mrs F. Hollands for kindly allowing them to reproduce on page 18 the photograph of the rainbow taken by her late husband.

A Studio Vista/Van Nostrand Reinhold How-to Book
Text copyright © 1972 by John Tuey and David Wickers
Drawings copyright © 1972 by Sharon Finmark
Photographs copyright © by Studio Vista

Photoset, printed and bound in England by
BAS Printers Limited, Hampshire

Published in Great Britain by
Studio Vista
Blue Star House, Highgate Hill, London N19
and in the United States by
Van Nostrand Reinhold Company
A Division of Litton Educational Publishing, Inc.
450 West 33rd Street, New York, NY 10001

Library of Congress Catalog Card Number 76-39848

ISBN 0 289 70243 7

Contents

Introduction

Scientific research today is a bewildering and complicated business. Most major scientific achievements are the result of work carried out in laboratories equipped with elaborate and expensive apparatus, such as electron microscopes and cyclotrons.

But many of the earlier discoveries, on which these modern advances are based, were made using much simpler equipment. Benjamin Franklin, for example, used a kite and a key to help him investigate the nature of lightning.

Even ordinary household materials, such as cardboard, wire and string, can be used to perform experiments which will help you to learn a little more about the world you live in. You will discover, by experiments, how and why certain everyday things happen in the way that they do, just as 'true' scientists experiment to investigate the nature of life itself.

As well as learning a little about science, you are sure to have a great deal of fun.

Air and space

You need:
candle
knife
large tumbler
matches
large, flat
cork

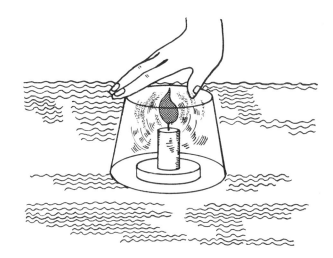

1 Cut a short length off the top of the candle and fix it to the cork with melted wax.

2 Fill the sink with water and float the cork on the surface. Light the candle.

3 Carefully lower the glass over the candle and push it down in the water. Be careful not to tip the glass to one side. The candle will sink into the water until even the flame itself is below the surface.

We all take it for granted that air exists. Although it cannot be seen like solids and liquids, it does take up space. In this experiment, the glass traps a pocket of air which prevents the water from rising into the glass to extinguish the candle. Because of the oxygen in the air the candle is able to burn under water!

Air and weight

You need:
pins   cotton
2 balloons   bamboo cane or long stick

1 Blow up the two balloons and tie one to each end of the cane with some cotton.

2 Pin a length of cotton to the ceiling and tie the other end round the centre of the cane so that the two balloons balance each other exactly.

3 Steady the cane with one hand and prick one of the balloons with a pin. Let go of the cane. It will tip up like a see-saw and the end with the inflated balloon will drop.

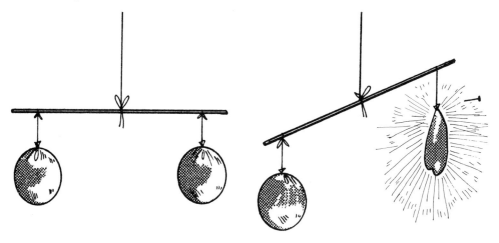

The burst balloon must have become lighter—but the only weight it can have lost is that of the air inside it. This shows that air not only takes up space but also has weight.

Vacuum

You need:
an old, large, metal can with a screw-on cap (do not use one that has contained any inflammable liquid unless it is thoroughly washed).

1 Pour a small amount of water in the can and boil it for about two minutes on the stove.

2 Turn off the heat. Hold the can with a thick cloth, and quickly screw the cap back on. Make sure that it is tight and leave the can to cool. After a while the can will begin to cave inwards.

When the water inside is boiling, the steam pushes the air out of the can. When it cools, the steam turns into water and there is no longer any air to support the sides of the can from the inside. This is known as a 'vacuum'. The strength of the air pressure on the sides of the can from the outside pushes them inwards and the can collapses.

Rust

You need:
jamjar   fine steel wool
a matchstick   dish

1 Roll a ball of steel wool in the palms of your hands above a piece of paper. Collect the little bits of steel together.

2 Rinse out the jamjar and tip the bits of steel wool into it. They will stick to the moist sides of the jar.

3 Pour some water into the dish (about 2.5 cm. or 1 in. deep). Stand the jamjar upside down in the dish with one side propped up by the matchstick. After about two or three days, the water will have risen in the jamjar and the steel wool will have turned brown with rust.

Both water and oxygen are needed to cause rust. Oxygen from the air trapped in the jar combines with the moisture to attack the steel and make rust. The water rises up into the jamjar to take the place of the oxygen that has been used up in this process. When the water no longer rises in the jar, all the oxygen, about one-fifth of the trapped air, will have been used up.

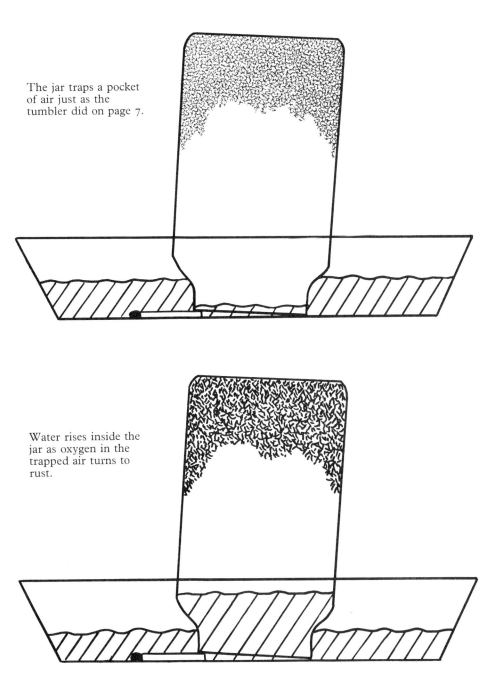

The jar traps a pocket of air just as the tumbler did on page 7.

Water rises inside the jar as oxygen in the trapped air turns to rust.

Fogs and mists

You need:
2 bricks
metal baking tray
large cup
piece of rag
drinking straw
ice
salt
matches

1 Stand the two bricks up on end. Fill the baking tray with ice and some salt, and stand it across the top of the bricks.

2 Fill the cup with hot water and place it beneath the tray. Blow into the water through a straw and a mist will form between the cup and the tray.

3 Set fire to the rag and blow out the flame. Hold the smouldering end between the cup and the tray and again blow into the hot water through the straw. This time a denser, dirtier fog will occur.

The hot water gives off a vapour which is cooled by the cold air around the baking tray. As the temperature falls, minute droplets of water appear because cold air cannot hold as much water vapour as warm air. This is why 'condensation' appears on the inside of windows on cold days. When the smoke from the smouldering rag is mixed with these water droplets, the mist becomes dirty just like real fog. Fog usually occurs in cities because of the dirt from factory chimneys and car exhausts. When it is very dirty it is called 'smog'.

Colour magic

You need:
a beetroot or red cabbage   vinegar
baking powder   2 white saucers
knife   saucepan

1 Chop the beetroot or red cabbage into small pieces and put them in a saucepan. Add a glassful of water and let it boil gently for a few minutes.

2 Pour some of this liquid into each saucer. Stir some baking powder into one of the saucers and watch the liquid change from red to green.

3 Add a few drops of vinegar to the liquid in the other saucer and stir. The colour will remain red.

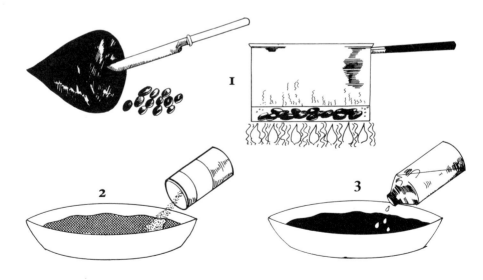

The baking powder and the vinegar represent two opposite types of substances in chemistry. The powder has the effect of a 'base' or 'alkali', and the vinegar of an 'acid'. The beetroot acts as an 'indicator' and changes colour when a base is added. The indicator does not change colour when an acid is added.

You could use this test on some other household substances such as lemon or orange juice, ammonia, liquid soap, onion, sour milk, cider, tomato etc. to see whether they are acids or bases. You could then use other indicators, such as the dyes that can be obtained from brightly coloured flowers. You will find that some of these produce different colour changes when the acids or bases are added.

Crystal gardens

You need:

jamjar	thin galvanized wire
saucepan	assorted crystals
sugar	large glass jar or tank
pencil	waterglass
cotton	spoon
paperclip	

1 Boil about 15 fl. oz. (just under a pint) of water in the saucepan and turn the heat low so that it simmers.

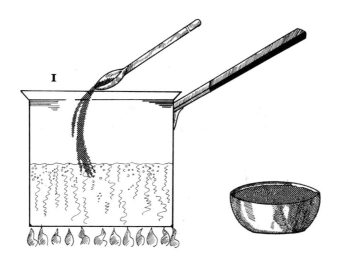

2 Stir in some sugar and keep adding it little by little until no more will dissolve. Pour the liquid carefully into the jamjar.

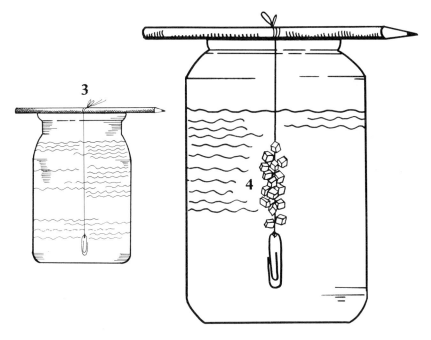

3 Knot a short piece of cotton onto the centre of a pencil and tie the other end round a paperclip. Lower the clip into the liquid and lay the pencil across the top of the jamjar.

4 Place the jamjar where it will not be disturbed. Crystals will form and grow into strange shapes on the cotton.

More sugar can be dissolved in hot water than in cold, and so, when the liquid cools, the extra dissolved sugar turns into crystals again.

Instead of using cotton, you might like to try bending lengths of galvanized wire into stars, crosses and other patterns for the crystals to grow on.

The spectacular photograph on the facing page was taken in north-west Scotland. Read how to make your own rainbow on page 22.

You can grow even more spectacular crystals that look like a colourful garden.

1 Three quarters fill a large glass jar (or aquarium tank) with hot water. Add enough waterglass to fill the jar and stir. Leave it to cool.

2 When the liquid is cold, drop in a variety of crystals.

You can use any of the following: alum, copper sulphate, copper nitrate, lead nitrate, ferrous sulphate, ferrous chloride, nickel sulphate, cobalt chloride, cobalt nitrate, epsom salts, aluminium sulphate, sodium thiosulphate (hypo). Most of these would be available from a chemist or drugstore or from a store selling junior chemistry sets.

3 Place the jar where it will not be disturbed.

After a while the crystals will begin to look like underwater coral. They will start to dissolve in the water, but because the waterglass prevents the particles from moving about, they will slowly reform into odd shapes.

Rainbow

You need:
a small mirror and a dish

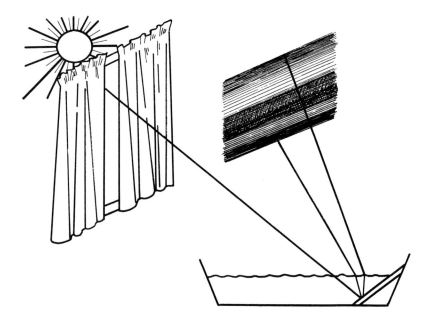

1 Fill the dish with water. Stand it on a table near a window so that the sun shines directly on it. Darken the room a little by drawing the curtains, leaving just a small gap for the sunlight to fall on the dish.

2 Place the mirror in the water with one edge resting on the side of the dish. Adjust the angle of the mirror so that a 'rainbow' appears on the wall or ceiling.

Sir Isaac Newton was the first to discover that the rays of the sun are made up from the seven basic 'rainbow' colours: red, orange, yellow, green, blue, indigo and violet. This is called the 'spectrum'. When the sunlight is bent or 'refracted' at an angle through the water it divides up into a spectrum because each basic colour is bent at a different angle. Real rainbows occur when sunlight passes through millions of raindrops and is broken into the spectrum colours. (There is a spectacular colour photograph of a rainbow on page 18.)

You can also make these rainbow colours merge and turn white. Divide a circle of cardboard into seven equal areas and colour each one a spectrum colour. Push a nail through the centre and spin the 'top'.

Periscope

You need:
long cardboard tube
    (from fabric shop)
2 small mirrors
small saw
square piece of paper
adhesive tape

1 Lay the cardboard tube diagonally across the square of paper, close to one end (see facing page).

2 Lift up the two corners of paper that are sticking out and wrap them round the tube. Stick these two corners together with adhesive tape.

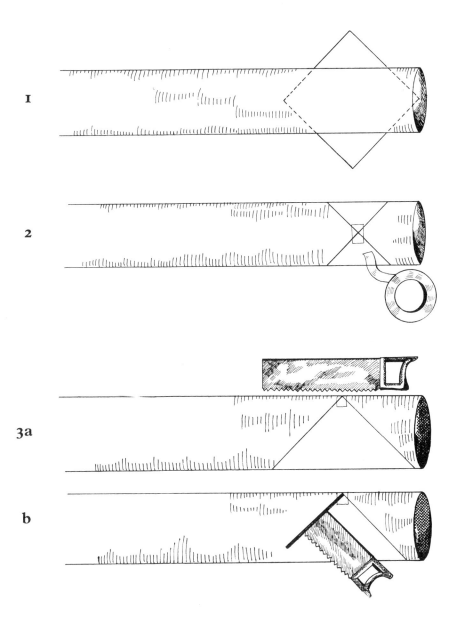

I

2

3a

b

3 Roll the tube so that the piece of adhesive tape is on top. Saw down towards the centre of the tube following the line of the paper. Stop sawing three-quarters of the way through the tube.

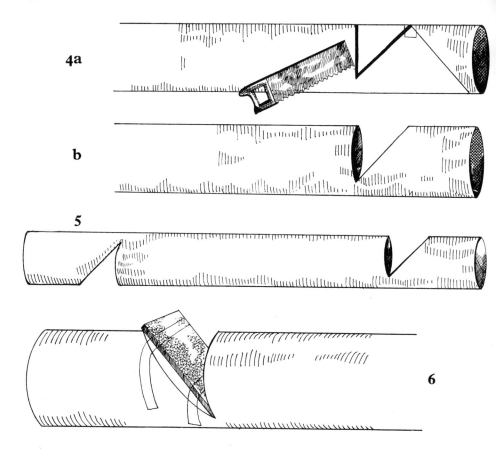

4a

b

5

6

4 Saw a straight line down from a point exactly above the end of the sloping saw cut. Remove the section that has been cut out.

5 Turn the tube over so that the cut you have made is underneath. Slide the paper down to the other end of the tube and saw in exactly the same way as before (but this time the saw cuts will be on the opposite side of the tube).

6 Lay the mirrors along the sloping cut edges, with the reflecting side facing outwards. Stick them to the sides of the tube with adhesive tape.

Hold the periscope upright and look into the lower mirror. You will be able to see up the tube, and out the other end. If you hide behind a wall with the periscope just peeping out over the top you will be able to see what is happening the other side without being visible to other people.

Light rays from the object you are looking at are reflected from one mirror onto the other and then to your eyes. Submarines use periscopes to enable the crew to see above the surface of the water while the boat is still submerged. The arrows show the lines along which the light travels.

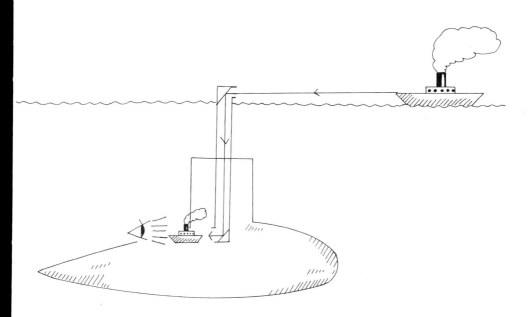

Images

You need:
greaseproof paper
cardboard box
adhesive tape
a dark cloth
ruler
pencil
a large pin

1 Remove the lid from the cardboard box. Stretch the greaseproof paper across the top and stick it down tightly with adhesive tape.

2 On the bottom of the box draw two diagonal lines from corner to corner to find the centre. Make a hole with the pin at this point.

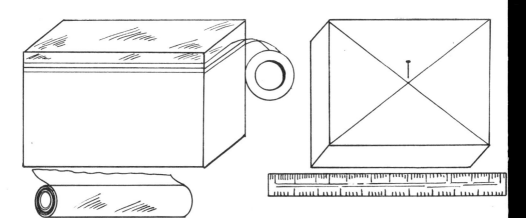

3 Place the box on a table in front of the window, with the pinhole pointing towards the window. Drape a dark cloth over your head and the end of the box so that the light can only enter through the pinhole. When you look at the greaseproof paper you will see a picture of the view outside the window . . . but it will be upside down!

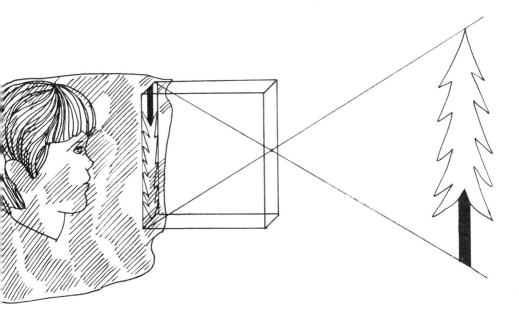

The picture will be fairly dark, but if you make the pinhole bigger to allow more light to enter the box the picture will become blurred. Both cameras and our eyes work in a similar way except that they have lenses to get a brighter but still a sharp picture. We really do 'see' the world upside down but our brains are able to turn the picture the other way round.

Hot air balloon see cover photograph

You need:
5 sheets of tissue paper
   50 × 75 cm. (20 × 30 in.)
paste
paperclips
scissors
cotton wool
cardboard
thick fuse wire
methylated spirit or
   rubbing alcohol
ruler

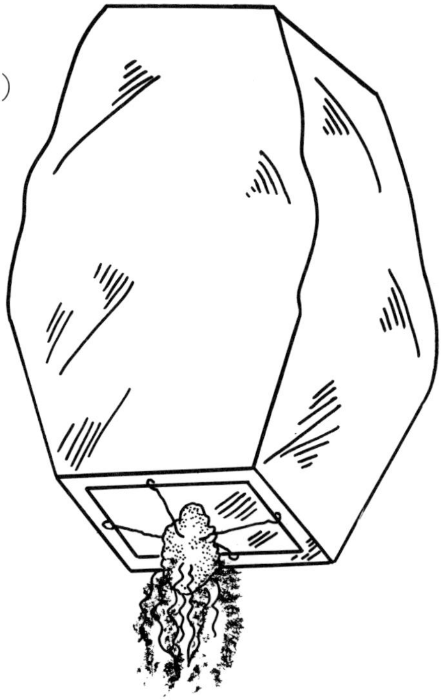

1 Lay four sheets of tissue paper on top of each other and hold them together with paperclips. Fold the tissue in half lengthwise, and then into four across the other way. Unfold the tissue and cut the corners off one end as shown in the diagram, cutting through four thicknesses.

2 Cut the fifth sheet of tissue paper into a square by trimming off the extra length. Place this square on some old newspaper and paste one of the shaped sheets onto each edge (diagram 2). Let the edges overlap about 1 cm. (or $\frac{1}{2}$ in.).

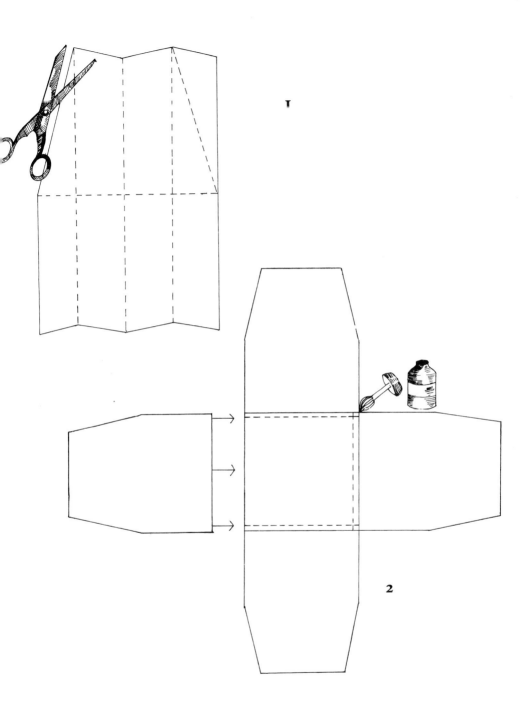

I

2

3 Paste along the sides of the tissue paper sections. Lift up two sections and pinch all along the edges so that they stick together. Repeat this with with other two sections so that they all form a large open bag.

4 Cut a square of cardboard, slightly larger than the open end of the bag or 'balloon', and cut out its centre leaving a frame of card 2.5 cm. (or 1 in.) wide.

5 Cut two lengths of wire 35 cm. (14 in.) long. Push each of them through a small ball of cotton wool so that they form a cross. Place the cross on the cardboard frame and twist the ends of the wire round the frame to hold it in place.

6 Hold the completed frame inside the neck of the balloon and paste the edges of tissue paper onto the frame.

On a day when there is no wind, take the hot air balloon and methylated spirit or rubbing alcohol into a large open space, well away from any buildings. Ask your father to help you launch the balloon. Blow into the balloon to remove any creases and soak the cotton wool with meths or alcohol, taking care not to wet the balloon itself. One of you can hold the balloon upright while the other sets fire to the cotton wool. Wait until you can feel the balloon lifting and then let go. It will rise into the sky because the heated air inside the balloon is lighter than the air surrounding it.

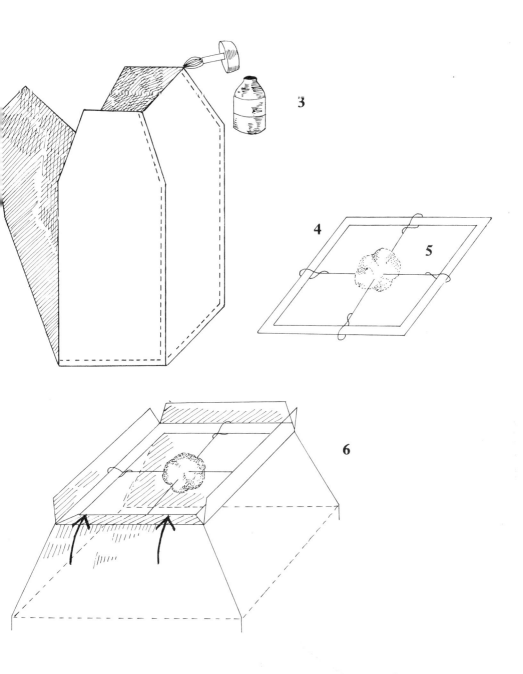

3

4

5

6

Fire extinguisher

You need:
glass coffee jar with lid
baking powder
vinegar
liquid detergent
cigar tube
cotton or wool
adhesive tape
hammer
nail
Plasticine

1 Tie a short length of
cotton or wool round the
open end of the cigar tube
and stick it down with
adhesive tape.

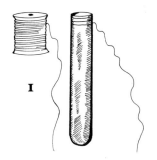

2 Three-quarters fill the
jar with vinegar and add a
small quantity of liquid
detergent.

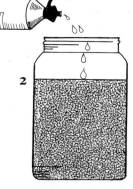

3 Make a hole in the lid of the jar with a nail.

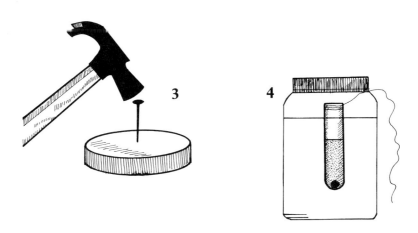

4 Put some Plasticine in the cigar tube (to give it some weight) and half fill it with baking powder. Lower the tube into the jar until about two-thirds of its length is in the liquid. Hold onto the cotton and replace the cap on the jar so that it traps the cotton.

Light a small fire of paper and twigs (ask your parents where you can do this safely). Now tilt the jar to set off your fire extinguisher.

When the jar is tilted, the baking powder mixes with the vinegar and gives off carbon dioxide gas. This makes the detergent foam up and pressure drives the foam out of the hole in a jet which smothers the fire. The oxygen in the air can no longer reach the flames and the fire is extinguished.

Electro-magnets can lift heavy loads very easily. Instructions for making your own simple electro-magnet are on page 54.

Hot rods and thermometers

You need:

metal rod (brass curtain rail
  or thick galvanized wire)
candle
scissors
clear drinking straw
bottle with a cork that
  fits the neck tightly

2 cans (the same size)
piece of card
2 knitting needles
glue
Plasticine
coloured ink

1 Cut a pointer from a piece of card and carefully push a knitting needle through the centre. Glue it in position (diagram 1, facing page).

2 Push a table against the wall. Stand the two cans on the table and lay the rod across them so that one end touches the wall.

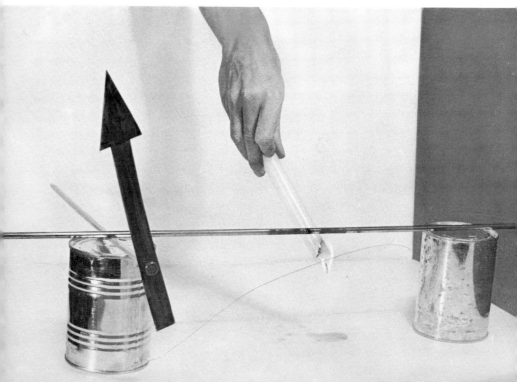

3 Lay the knitting needle and pointer under the rod and across the can that is furthest from the wall. Turn the needle so that the card points straight up.

4 Move a lighted candle slowly up and down under the length of the rod. Watch the pointer move as the rod grows hot and begins to expand.

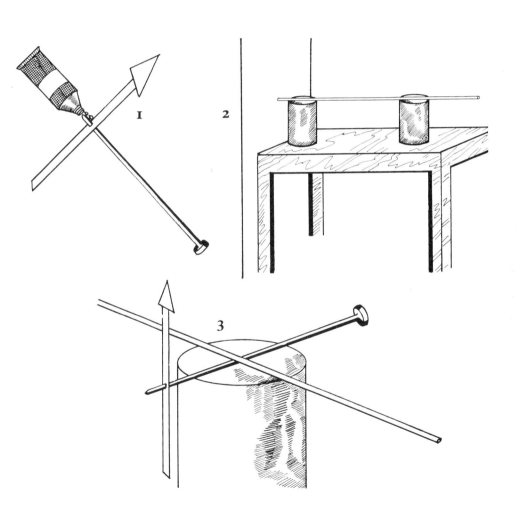

Liquids also expand as they grow hot. By making a simple thermometer you will be able to see the effect of heat on a liquid.

1 Make a hole through the centre of a cork with a knitting needle and then push a drinking straw through the hole.

2 Pour some coloured ink into the bottle and fill it right to the top with water.

3 Push the cork and straw into the neck of the bottle. Do this over a sink in case some liquid is squeezed out. Make sure that air cannot enter the bottle by sealing any gaps around the cork and straw with Plasticine.

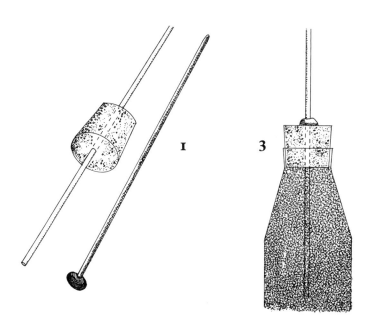

1   3

4 Place the bottle on a hot radiator and the water will rise in the straw as it expands. When the bottle is removed from the heat the level will fall.

Although this one does not tell you the exact temperature, a real thermometer works in the same way.

Both solids and liquids are made up of billions of tiny particles called 'molecules'. These are moving around the whole time although they are invisible even through powerful micro-scopes. When they are heated they move much faster and take up more room.

This means that the heated liquid in the bottle takes up more room and rises inside the straw as the water molecules move faster. The rod grows slightly fatter and longer as the metal molecules do the same. This is why railway lines have small gaps between each length of rail to allow for expansion during a hot summer.

Flying boat

You need:
empty cigar tube
rectangular metal tin
   about 2.5 cm. (1 in.) deep
pipe cleaners
candle

adhesive tape
hammer
a small nail
knife

1 Remove the cap from the cigar tube and make a small hole towards the edge of the cap using the nail.

2 Half fill the cigar tube with hot water and replace the cap.

3 Twist a pipe cleaner round each end of the cigar tube. Hold the tube above the tin and hook the ends of the pipe cleaners over the edges. Make sure that the hole in the cap is near the top so that the water does not trickle out. Stick adhesive tape over the pipe cleaners to hold the tube in place.

4 Cut off a short length of candle and place it on the tin beneath the middle of the cigar tube. Float the 'flying boat' in a bath of water (or pond) and light the candle. After a few minutes the water will boil and a jet of steam will escape from the hole in the cap. The escaping steam exerts a force that drives the 'flying boat' forward.

The force produces a reaction in the opposite direction. (In other words, the steam is escaping towards the right of the photograph, but the 'flying boat' is moving to the left.) This principle was discovered by Sir Isaac Newton in the seventeenth century. The engines of a modern jet aircraft work in a similar way.

Scales and pulleys

You need:
small cardboard tube
galvanized wire
strong elastic band
pliers
pencil
knife
scissors
cotton reels or spools
broom handle
string

1 Using the pliers, cut a length of galvanized wire slightly longer than the width of the tube. Make a small hole in the side of the tube at one end. Make a second small hole opposite it.

2 Push the wire through one hole, thread the elastic band onto it, and push it through the other hole. Bend down both ends of the wire to hold it in place. Cut a narrow slit up one side of the tube as far as the free end of the elastic band.

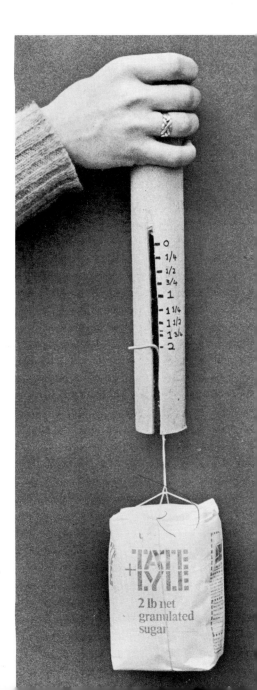

3 Cut a short length of galvanized wire a little longer than the slot, and bend it into two hooks as shown in diagram **3a**. Hook the end with the 'pointer' to the elastic band.

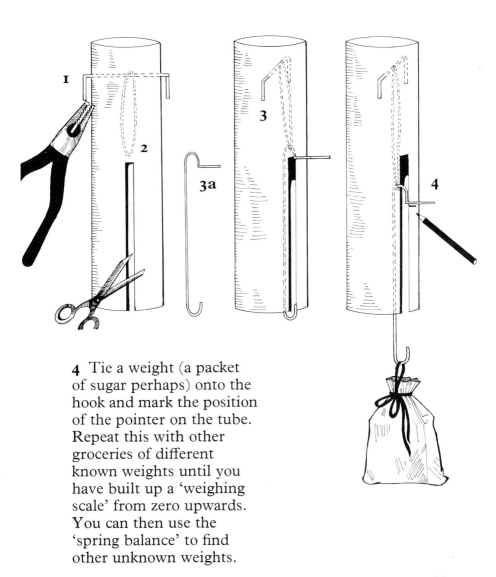

4 Tie a weight (a packet of sugar perhaps) onto the hook and mark the position of the pointer on the tube. Repeat this with other groceries of different known weights until you have built up a 'weighing scale' from zero upwards. You can then use the 'spring balance' to find other unknown weights.

5 Bend about 30 cm. (1 ft.) of galvanized wire into a triangle, with a small gap in the middle of one side. Push the two ends into a cotton reel or spool.

6 Place a broom handle across the backs of two chairs. Tie one end of a length of string round the broom handle, pass it through the triangle, round the cotton reel, and tie the other end to the hook of the spring balance.

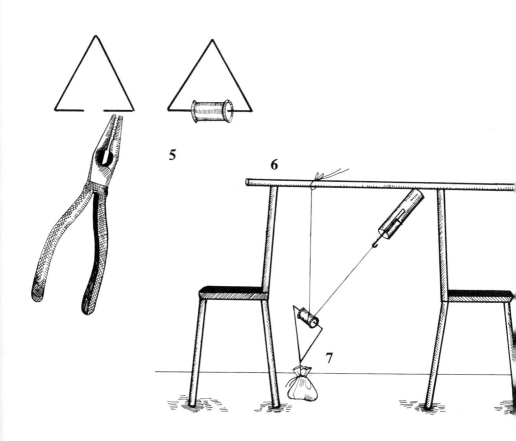

7 Attach the same packet of sugar to the triangle with some string and pull the weight upwards with the spring balance.

The pointer on the spring balance will no longer reach the same mark as before. The weight itself has not changed so you know it must still weigh the same— but the load has become easier to lift because of the pulley.

Tractor

You need:
an empty, wooden
   cotton reel or spool
elastic band
drawing pin or thumbtack
long nail
candle
knife
matchstick

1 Cut a narrow strip off the end of the candle with the knife. (You may have to heat the knife so that it cuts easily.) Make a hole through the centre with the nail.

2 Cut notches round both rims of the cotton reel or spool and thread the elastic band through the centre.

3 Push a tack in one end of the reel and loop the elastic over it. Thread the other end of the band through the piece of candle. Thread the matchstick through the loop.

4 Wind up the elastic by twisting the match round and round. Hold the match and place the tractor on a carpet. As the elastic begins to unwind, the tractor will move slowly across the floor.

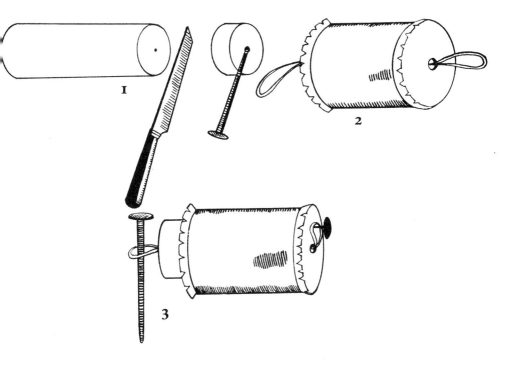

When the elastic band is wound up, the tractor is given a store of 'energy' which enables it to move when the match is released. The notches round the edge of the reel grip the surface of the carpet, rather like the tread of rubber tyres on a road.

Finding North

You need:
a bar magnet
razor blade
white card
glue
scissors
ball-point pen

compasses
protractor
large cork
needle
ruler

1 Draw a circle 7.5 cm. (3 in.) in diameter. Using the protractor, draw two lines through the centre at right angles to each other. Then draw two more lines to divide the circle into eight equal sections.

2 Carefully cut out the circle. Draw the lines on the other side of the card in exactly the same positions as before.

3 Magnetize the razor blade by stroking one end of the magnet along the length of the blade. Move the magnet in the same direction each time, keeping it well clear of the razor blade in between each stroke. Be careful not to cut yourself on the sharp edges.

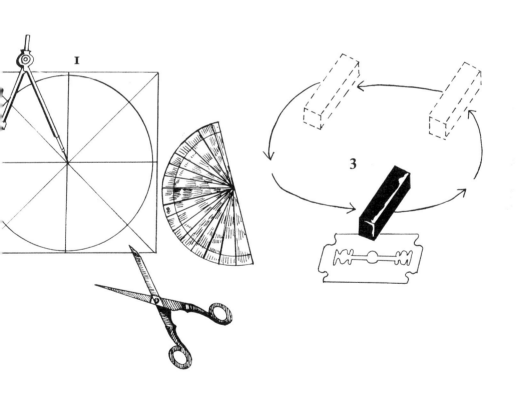

4 Push the needle through the centre of the cork.

5 Using the point of the ball-point pen, make a dent in the centre of the card circle where the lines cross.

6 Glue the razor blade to this side of the card so that the slot in the blade lies directly over one of the lines and the dent you have made is exactly in the centre.

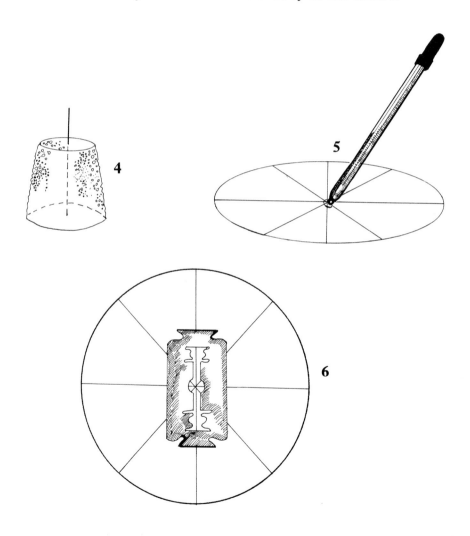

7 Balance the card on the needle with the razor blade on the underside (if it tips up try adding some Plasticine to balance it). The card will turn and settle in one position. Find out which of the lines indicates north from where you stand and mark the 'points' of the compass; North, South, East and West.

Steel contains billions of 'molecules' which act as tiny magnets, all pointing in different directions (diagram **a**). When you stroke the razor blade with the much more powerful magnet, the smaller ones are attracted to it and all line up in the same direction (**b**). Acting together in this way, they make the razor blade itself into a magnet.

The earth is surrounded by lines of magnetic force and the razor blade magnet is influenced by them. The North pole of the earth attracts the north-seeking end of the magnet and so, no matter where you go, your compass will always be able to find North.

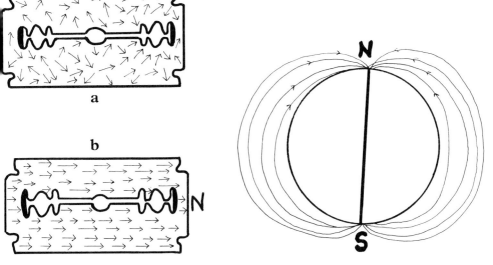

a

b

N

S

Electro-magnet

You need:
a strong battery
piece of bell wire
   2 m. (6 ft.) long
steel nut and bolt
   8–10 cm. (3–4 in.)
   long
knife
adhesive tape

1 Beginning about 30 cm. (1 ft.) from the end of the wire, wind it tightly round the bolt. Start at the head of the bolt and wind towards the nut, making sure that each turn of the wire lies next to the one before it.

2 When you reach the end of the bolt, wind back to the head again. Cover the bolt in two or three layers of wire. Stop winding about 30 cm. (1 ft.) from the end of the wire. Stick down the last coil with adhesive tape.

3 Scrape off the plastic insulation from both ends of the wire with the knife and wind them round the two battery terminals.

Hold the electro-magnet over some paperclips and the end of the bolt will attract them in the same way as an ordinary magnet.

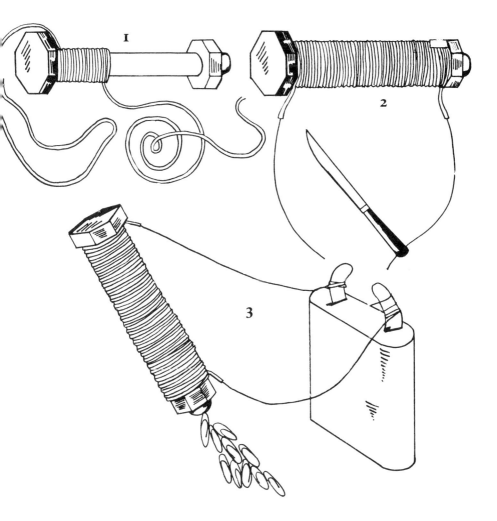

The electric current that flows along the wire from the
battery creates lines of magnetic force in the bolt.
Unlike the ordinary magnet, however, the electro-
magnet can be switched off simply by disconnecting
one of the battery leads. This makes it a useful device
in industry—cranes, for example, often have electro-
magnets instead of hooks with which to lift steel
objects and scrap metal (see colour photograph page
36).

Invisible power

You need:

metal baking tray	sponge
glass tumbler	scissors
balloon	foil from a pack
plastic comb	of cigarettes
galvanized wire	an empty coffee jar
jamjar	

1 Stand the baking tray on the tumbler and blow up the balloon and tie the neck. Rub it several times on a woollen sweater and place it on the tray.

2 Hold your finger near the baking tray and a small spark will jump across to it—the equivalent of several thousand volts!

The spark is, of course, harmless. Although the 'voltage' is high, the quantity of electricity is very small because it is 'static', produced by friction when the balloon is rubbed against the wool. You can test these weak static charges by making a simple electroscope.

1

2

3 Push a length of galvanized wire through the centre of the sponge and bend the end into an 'L' shape.

4 Cut a small, narrow strip of foil and fold it in half lengthwise over the hook of the 'L'. Lower the wire into the jar so that the sponge rests on the rim.

5 Pass the comb through your hair a few times and bring it close to the wire. The foil will open out to show that electricity is present. You can 'discharge' the foil (rid it of electricity) simply by touching the wire with your hand.

Lightning is also the result of static electricity. The friction in powerful air currents produces sparks and electrical charges of the same type, but of much more energy than in these experiments!

Electrifying journey

You need:
3 volt battery
3 volt bulb, bulb holder and screws
block of wood about 60 × 15 × 2.5 cm. (24 × 3 ×
    1 in.)
insulated bell wire about 1.5 m. (5 ft.) long
galvanized wire 1.5–2 m. (5–6 ft.) long
screwdriver; pliers; hammer and nail; penknife
adhesive tape

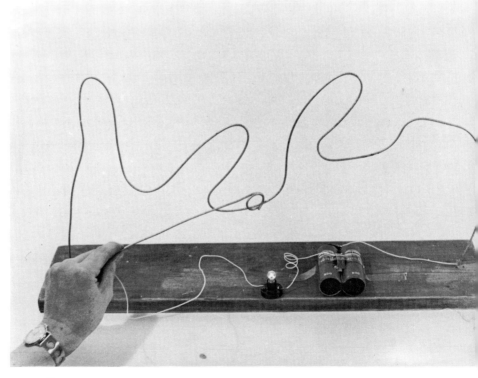

1 Hammer a nail into each end of the block of wood and remove it with the pliers. The galvanized wire should be able to fit into the holes made by the nail.

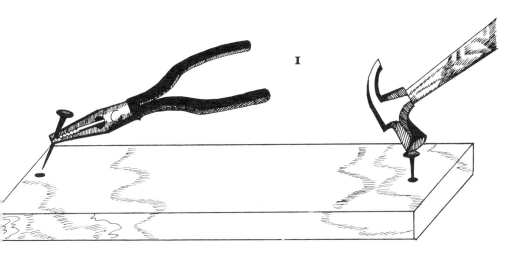

2 Screw the bulb holder to the centre of the wood. Place the battery alongside the bulb holder and stick it to the board with adhesive tape.

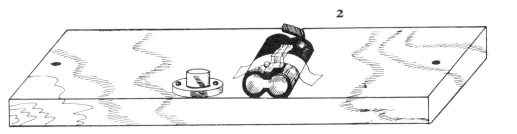

3 Cut off 30 cm. (1 ft.) of galvanized wire with the pliers and put it to one side.

4 Push one end of the remaining length of galvanized wire into one of the holes in the wood. Bend the rest into a series of curves so that it looks a little like the roller coasters you see in amusement parks.

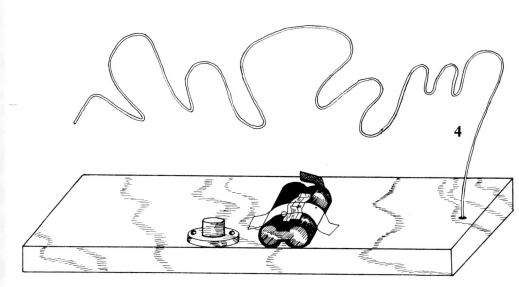

4

5 Bend the top of the small piece of galvanized wire into a small circle with the pliers and twist it round to hold it in position.

6 Cut a piece of bell wire 1.25 m. (4 ft.) long. Scrape the plastic from the ends with the penknife, **6a**. Use adhesive tape to attach one end to the 'handle' of the circle you have just made, **6b**. Attach the other end to one of the bulb holder terminals, **6c**.

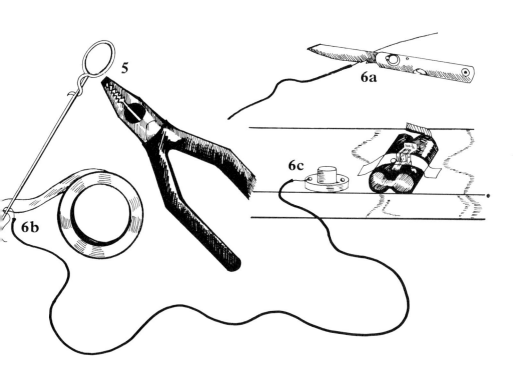

7 Thread the circle over the bending galvanized wire and push the free end of the wire into the second hole in the wood.

8 Scrape the plastic from the ends of a short piece of bell wire and attach one end to the second bulb holder terminal. Attach the other end to one of the battery terminals by twisting it round the brass plate and sticking it down with adhesive tape.

9 Scrape the plastic from another length of bell wire and connect one end to the second battery terminal in the same way as before. Twist the other end of the wire round the galvanized wire path where it goes into the wood. Screw the bulb into the holder.

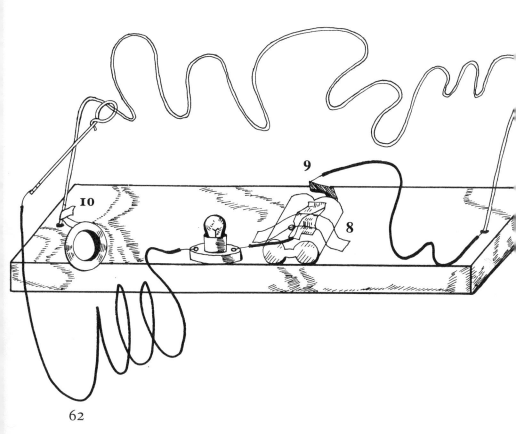

10 Wrap some adhesive tape round the other end of the galvanized wire path where it goes into the wood.

When the circle touches the bending wire path, the bulb will light up. See how steady your hand is by trying to steer the circle along the path from one end to the other, following round the bends, without lighting the bulb. If you find this easy, try making the circle smaller and the bends tighter.

The 'electrifying journey' is a simple, electrical 'circuit'. The bulb will only light up when the circuit is continuous. This occurs only when the circle touches the wire path. Electricity can then flow from one battery terminal to the other without a break, lighting up the bulb on its way.

When you have finished making your electrifying journeys, there is no need to disconnect the battery. Just place the circle over the end of the path where it is covered with adhesive tape. This will not be able to conduct electricity and, because the circuit is incomplete, the bulb will not light up.

Barometer

You need:
an empty tin can
large balloon
elastic bands
glue
drinking straw
paper
pins
scissors

1 Cut the top off the balloon and stretch the larger part across the open end of the can. Hold it in place with two or three elastic bands.

2 Glue one end of the straw to the centre of the rubber. When it is dry place the can on a table by a wall.

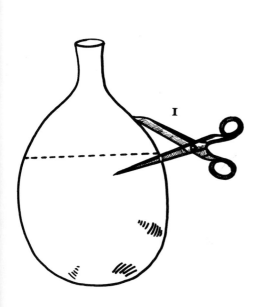

3 Pin a piece of paper onto the wall behind the other end of the straw. Draw a sun just above the tip of the straw and a rain cloud just below.

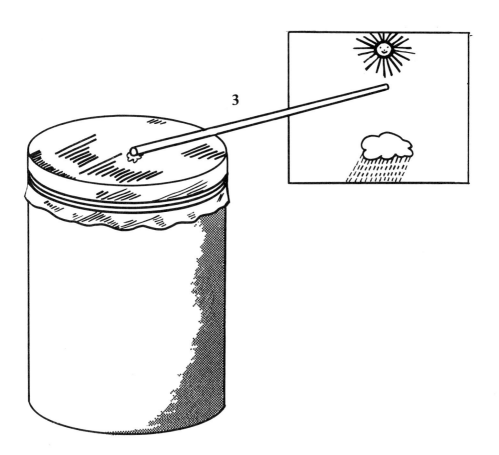

Because air has weight, it exerts a pressure in all directions. When the air pressure outside the can is greater than that of the air inside, the rubber will be pushed down and the straw will rise. When the opposite is true the straw will fall. Real barometers work in this way. You can expect the weather to be sunnier when the pressure is high and often rainy when it falls.

Sundial

You need:
knitting needle   pencil
cork   compasses
white card   scissors

1 Draw a large circle on the card and cut it out.

2 Push the knitting needle through the centre of the card and then through the cork. Slide the cork and card to the middle of the knitting needle so that they lie next to each other.

3 Push the knitting needle into the ground in a sunny area. At every hour mark the position made by the shadow of the knitting needle on the card (so that at 9 o'clock you put a mark with a '9' beside it and so on at every hour until sunset).

The sundial will work just like a clock (when the sun shines!) and you will be able to tell the time from the shadow of the knitting needle.

The earth travels once round the sun every year. It also spins round and round as it does so, each complete spin taking twenty-four hours. We do not feel the earth spinning but we can see that it does from the way the sun seems to move across the sky. As the sun 'moves', the angles of the shadows change and from this we can measure the passing of time.

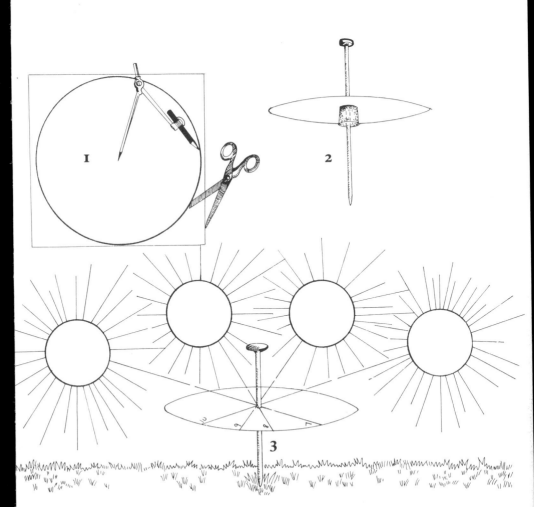

Index